Readers will get the
Key Words reading
follow the books in th
2a, 2b, 2c: and so on.

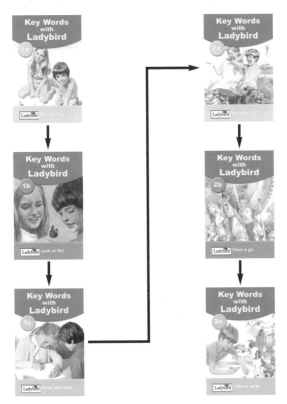

The a, b, and c series are all written using
the same carefully controlled vocabulary.

The Ladybird Key Words Reading Scheme
has three series, each containing
twelve books.

The 'a' series gradually introduces and
repeats new words.

The parallel 'b' series provides further
practice of these words, but in a different
context and with different illustrations.

The 'c' series uses familiar words to teach
phonics in a methodical way, enabling
children to read more difficult words. It also
provides a link with writing.

All three series are written using the same
carefully controlled vocabulary.

Published by Ladybird Books Ltd
A Penguin Company
Penguin Books Ltd., 80 Strand, London WC2R 0RL, UK
Penguin Books Australia Ltd., Camberwell, Victoria, Australia
Penguin Books (NZ) Ltd., Private Bag 102902, NSMC, Auckland, New Zealand

7 9 10 8 6

Printed in China

Key Words
Reading Scheme

5c
More sounds
to say

 g
n
 d

written by W. Murray
illustrated by J.H. Wingfield

The girl has some cards. Each card has a picture on it.

She looks at the picture on each card and puts it with the letter sound.

There are pictures of a boy, a cat, a top, an apple, a fish, a hat, a man, and the sun.

The letter sounds are **b**, **c**, **t**, **a**, **f**, **h**, **m**, and **s**.

Sounds we know from Book 4c

The boy has some cards. There is a picture on each card.

He looks at the picture on each card. Then he puts the card with the letter sound.

There are pictures of milk, some apples, a seat, a fire, a house, two, a car, and a bus.

The letter sounds are **m**, **a**, **s**, **f**, **h**, **t**, **c**, and **b**.

i

Here is some ink.
Say the word ink.
What is the sound
    when you start to say **ink**?

i

Here is an insect.
Say the word insect.
What is the sound
    when you start to say **insect**?

i

Here is an Indian.
Say the word Indian.
You make the **i** sound
    when you start to say **Indian**.

i

i

i

e

Here is an egg.
Say the word egg.
What is the sound
   when you start to say **egg**?

e

Here is an elephant.
Say the word elephant.
You make the **e** sound
   when you start to say **elephant**.

e

Here is an entrance.
Say the word entrance.
What is the sound
   when you start to say **entrance**?

e

Here is an exit.
Say the word exit.
You make the **e** sound
   when you start to say **exit**.

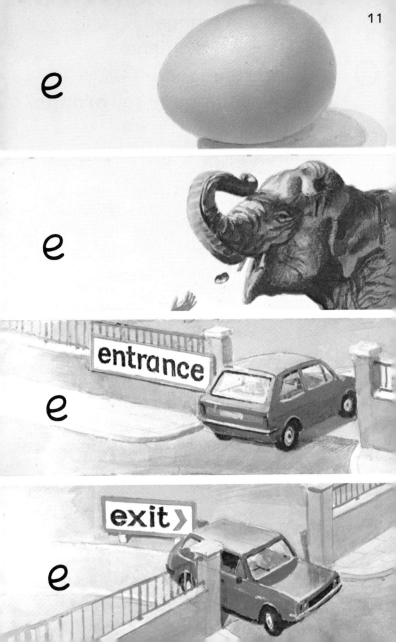

e

e

e

e

O

Here is an orange.
Say the word orange.
What is the sound
when you start to say **orange**?

O

Here is an ostrich.
Say the word ostrich.
You make the **o** sound
when you start to say **ostrich**.

O

Here is an ox.
Say the word ox.
What is the sound
when you start to say **ox**?

O

Here is an otter.
Say the word otter.
You make the **o** sound
when you start to say **otter**.

O

O

O

O

u

The boy is up.
Say the word up.
What is the sound
  when you start to say **up**?

u

The dog is under.
Say the word under.
You make the **u** sound
  when you start to say **under**.

u

It is an umbrella.
You say umbrella.
How do you start
  when you say **umbrella**?

u

Here is an umpire.
Say the word umpire.
You make the **u** sound
  when you start to say **umpire**.

u

u

u

u

You can read all the words when you
make the sounds—

1. Dan has some ham.
   The ham is not fat.

2. Jill has a hat.
   Jill has a cat.

3. Bob is in a hut.
   He has a bat.

4. It is hot.
   Tom is fit.

1

2   17

3

4

d

Here is a dog.

I can say dog.

It starts with **d**.

d

Here is a doll.

I can say doll.

It starts with **d**.

d

Here is a door.

I can say door.

It starts with **d**.

d

Here is a duck.

I can say duck.

It starts with **d**.

d

d

d

d

g

This is a girl.

We can say girl.

It starts with **g**.

g

This is a gun.

We can say gun.

It starts with **g**.

g

This is a gate.

We can say gate.

It starts with **g**.

g

This is a goose.

We can say goose.

It starts with **g**.

g

g

g

g

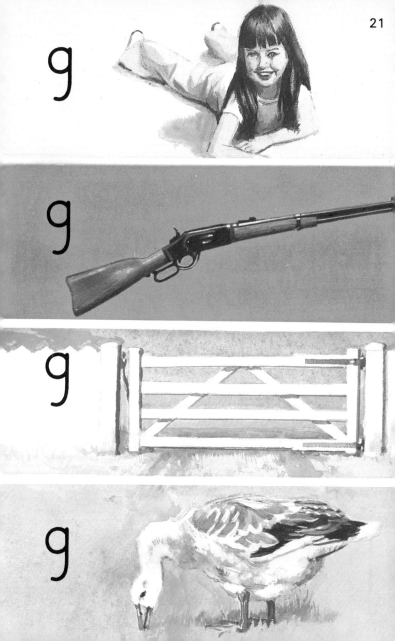

It is a letter.

You say letter.

It starts with **l**.

It is a log.

You say log.

It starts with **l**.

It is a leg.

You say leg.

It starts with **l**.

It is a lorry.

You say lorry.

It starts with **l**.

Miss Ladybird
Beeches Rd
Loughborough

n

We see a net.

We can say net.

It starts with **n**.

n

We see a nest.

We can say nest.

It starts with **n**.

n

We see a nine.

We can say nine.

It starts with **n**.

n

We see a nurse.

We can say nurse.

It starts with **n**.

n

n

n

n

You can read all the words when you
make the sounds—

1. The bag is big.
   It is a big bag.

2. The dog is hot.
   It is hot in the sun.

3. It is a cat.
   It is a fat cat.

4. He is fit.
   He is a fit man.

5. He has a bat.
   He puts the bat in the hut.

6. He has a tin.
   It is ham in the tin.

7. He is in bed.
   He has cut his leg.

8. The sun is hot.
   It is not hot in the hut.

Peter and Jane are going out this afternoon. They know a brother and sister who have a boat. The boy is Sam and the girl is Bess. Peter and Jane are going to see them this afternoon on the boat.

"We will go by bus and then walk there," says Peter. "I know how to get to the boat."

Copy out and complete—

1. Peter and Jane will —o by bus.

2. The —irl is Bess.

3. The boy —s Sam.

4. Peter and Jane —ike Sam and Bess.

The answers are on Page 48

Bus Stop

Peter says he knows which bus to take. Soon they are on the top of the bus as it is going up the street. They talk about the boat and about Sam and Bess.

They get off the bus and walk up a hill. "We'll see the boat from the top of the hill," says Peter.

Copy out and complete—

1. Peter says "Here —s the bus."

2. It is going —p the street.

3. They get —ff the bus.

4. They walk up the —ill.

The answers are on Page 48

As the brother and sister get to the top of the hill they look down at the water. Now they can see where the boat is.

Peter points to the water. "There it is," he says. "I said so. You can see it down there."

"We must go down now," says Jane. "Come on, let's run down to the water."

Copy out and complete—

1. They g—t to the top of the hill.

2. "There —t —s," says Peter.

3. "I can —ee it," says Jane.

4. She says, "We must go down —ow."

The answers are on Page 48

Peter and Jane run down to the water. They soon get there. Then the other children on the boat see Peter and Jane.

"Dad will come and get you in our little boat," says Sam.

Peter and Jane see Sam's dad get into the little boat.

"Here he comes," says Peter. "He will take us to the boat."

Copy out and complete—

1. Bess and Sam are —n the boat.

2. Peter and Jane —ook at the boat.

3. "Dad will come and —et you," says Sam.

4. Peter says,"He will —ake us to the boat."

The answers are on Page 49

Jane and Peter are with Sam's dad in the little boat. They will soon be on the boat with Sam and Bess.

"It's a big boat," says Jane. "I like it."

"It's good of you to ask us to come," says Peter to Sam's dad.

"We like to have you with us," he says. "You must come again."

Copy out and complete—

1. Peter and Jane are —n the water.

2. Sam's —ad has a little boat.

3. The boat is a —ig —oat.

4. Peter and Jane —ike the boat.

The answers are on Page 49

The four children are on the big boat. The girls look on, as the boys fish.

Sam has a fish in his hand. "This makes five," he says.

"Some girls fish," says Bess, "but I do not like to."

"No," says Jane, "I do not want to fish. Let the boys do the work."

Sam's mum and dad sit on chairs in the sun.

Copy out and complete—

1. The girls —o —ot like to fish.

2. Sam has a fish in —is —and.

3. The boys have —ive —ish.

4. Sam's mum and dad —it in the —un.

The answers are on Page 49

Jane helps Bess and her mum to get the tea. She likes to do this.

The two boys play on the boat.

Peter says he is the look-out. "I see some more boats from here," he says.

Sam says, "Look at me. I can make the boat go."

Bess looks out. "Come in for tea," she says.

Copy out and complete—

1. Jane —elps to get the —ea.

2. "I will —e the look-out," says Peter.

3. Sam says, "Look —t —e."

4. Bess says, "—ome in for tea."

The answers are on Page 50

They eat eggs or fish for tea. After they have had tea, Sam's dad says that they are going to the shops. He gives the children some money.

"Help me to start the boat," he says to the boys. Sam and Peter pull in the little boat.

Sam's dad starts the big boat, and soon it is going by the other boats.

Copy out and complete—

1   I like to eat —ggs.

2.   "Let —s help Dad," says Sam.

3.   Sam's —ad starts the boat.

4.   Jane has a —et.

The answers are on Page 50

Sam says that one afternoon he saw a little boy in danger in the water. "I ran to get some men to help," he says.

"I was there," says Bess. "I saw the men pull the little boy out of the water."

Soon they all come to the shops. They look in the windows and then they go into a shop.

Copy out and complete—

1. Sam —aw the little boy.

2. The —oy was in the water.

3. "I ran to g—t some m—n," Sam says.

4. Bess says, "I saw the men —elp the boy."

The answers are on Page 50

They are all in the shop. Bess wants a hat for the boat. The girl in the shop has four or five hats that Bess likes.

Jane sees a little pig in the shop. "Look," she says to Bess. "You can put money in this little pig."

The boys look at things for boats. They talk to the man in the shop about them.

Copy out and complete—

1. Bess wants a —at.

2. You —an put —oney in the pig.

3. The boys are —n the shop.

4. They look at things —or boats.

The answers are on Page 50

Pages 48 to 50 give the answers to the written exercises in the book.

Page 28 1 Peter and Jane will go by bus.

2 The girl is Bess.

3 The boy is Sam.

4 Peter and Jane like Sam and Bess.

Page 30 1 Peter says, "Here is the bus."

2 It is going up the street.

3 They get off the bus.

4 They walk up the hill.

Page 32 1 They get to the top of the hill.

2 "There it is," says Peter.

3 "I can see it," says Jane.

4 She says, "We must go down now."

Page 34 1   Bess and Sam are on the boat.

            2   Peter and Jane look at the boat.

            3   "Dad will come and get you," says Sam.

            4   Peter says, "He will take us to the boat."

Page 37 1   Peter and Jane are on the water.

            2   Sam's dad has a little boat.

            3   The boat is a big boat.

            4   Peter and Jane like the boat.

Page 39 1   The girls do not like to fish.

            2   Sam has a fish in his hand.

            3   The boys have five fish.

            4   Sam's mum and dad sit in the sun.

Page 40 1 Jane helps to get the tea.

2 "I will be the look-out," says Peter.

3 Sam says, "Look at me."

4 Bess says, "Come in for tea."

Page 42 1 I like to eat eggs.

2 "Let us help Dad," says Sam.

3 Sam's dad starts the boat.

4 Jane has a net.

Page 45 1 Sam saw the little boy.

2 The boy was in the water.

3 "I ran to get some men," Sam says.

4 Bess says, "I saw the men help the boy."

Page 47 1 Bess wants a hat.

2 You can put money in the pig.

3 The boys are in the shop.

4 They look at things for boats.

Revision—

a	**e**	**i**	**o**	**u**
apple	egg	is	on	us
as	elephant	in	off	up
at	entrance	ink	orange	under
an	exit	inch	ostrich	umbrella
and		insect	ox	umpire
away		Indian	otter	

d	**g**	**l**	**n**
dog	get	let	net
doll	game	leg	nest
door	gate	letter	nine
duck	girl	log	no
Dad	goose.	look	not
	gun	lorry	now
			nurse

Sounds from Book 4c

a   b   c   f   h   m   s   t

Now read Book 6a

Learning by sounds

If children learn the sounds of letters and how to blend them with the other letter sounds (eg. c-a-t) they can tackle new words independently (eg. P-a-t).

In the initial stages it is best if these phonic words are already known to the learner.

However, not all English words can be learned in this way as the English language is not purely phonetic (eg. t-h-e).

In general a 'mixed' approach to reading is recommended. Some words are learned by blending the sounds of their letters and others by look-and-say, whole word or sentence methods.

This book provides the link with writing for the words in Readers 5a and 5b.